What to Do When You're Feeling Blue

Andi Cann

What to do when you're feeling blue is a rhyming book meant to help children enjoy happy feelings and cope with feelings of sadness.

Children (and even adults) are sometimes overwhelmed by their emotions. They may not understand why one moment they are happy and at another moment they are sad.

This book is meant to help children understand their emotions and offers strategies to cope with sadness.   Its intent is to introduce a discussion between children and parents about happiness and sadness.

There are a few subtle clues about the reason for sadness like the introduction of "season" as a potential reason for sadness, for people who are affected by seasonal affective disorder when there is less sun.

Mostly, the book offers reminders to children they are important and there are family and friends who love them no matter how they feel!

If you or your family members need help with ongoing sadness or depression, contact the National Alliance for Mental Illness at 800-950-6264 or text NAMI in a crisis at 741741.

For all the parents who support their children and teach them how to cope with emotions.

Hi! My name is Kappy and I love being happy!

I dance with feet that are quite tap, tap,

tap,

tappy.

I love balloons, my little brother, and our dog.

I play at the pond and smile at the frog.

I like it when I'm happy. It feels zippy.

It feels zappy.

I smile at everyone and hold them tight.

I give them compliments and make the day bright.

But sometimes I'm sad...

And I

don't

know

what to

do.

How do I stop feeling so very, very blue?

I don't feel like dancing or going to the zoo. What can I do when my heart has a boo boo?

My dad says feeling sad is okay.

But, I ask him, but what if I just want to

feel better

THAT

day?

He says, I can play with my cat or go to story time.

I can ride a bike or eat a carrot.

It's even okay to whine.

But I wondered why am I sad? Why aren't I mad? Or even glad? I asked my mom, since I already asked my dad. And she said...

Sometimes you're sad because it's the season.

Other times it's a feeling you have for no reason.

But, if you're feeling sad, there are things you can do to feel better.

You can read a book, be with a friend, talk to your mom, or play pretend.

You can think about things that make you happy like apples and sunshine and dancing with a friend...

And daydreams, and night dreams, and bad dreams that end.

Soon,
you'll feel
calm and
remember
something
true.

Feelings
are feelings that change… sometimes…
no matter what you do.

So, take a deep breath and think about your friends, imagine the wonders you will see around the bend.

Think about a whale with a moon balanced on its nose.

Picture a polar
bear with icy
crystals that he
blows.

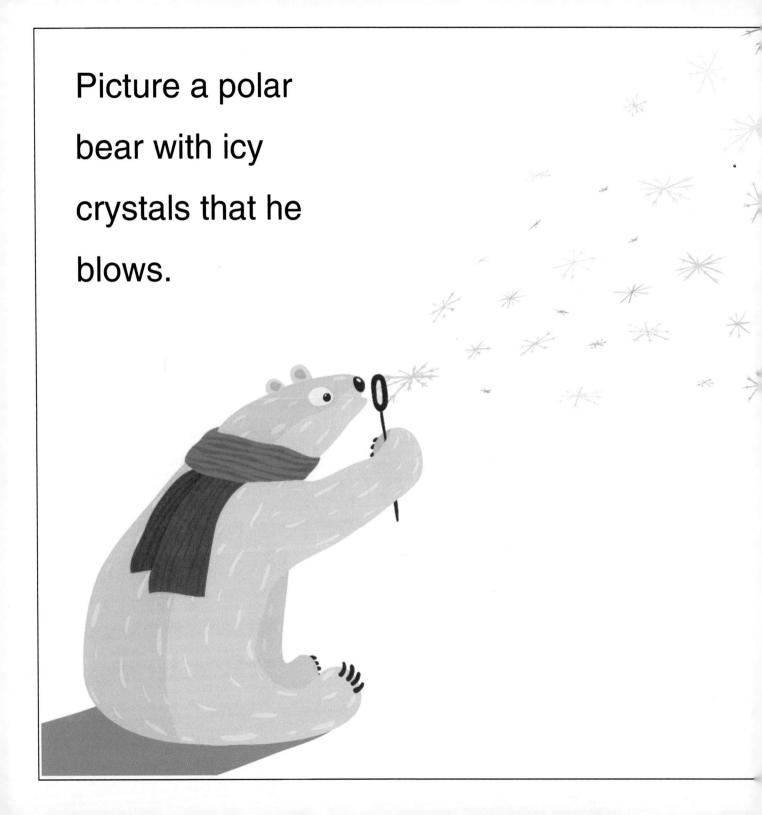

Into a frosty night with hugs, smiles, and a scarf that you knit!

Remember fun with your friends and know that you will be sad for just a little bit.

Picture adventures, your family, and a whole lot of love.

And story times and smiles
and a colorful dove.

No matter how you feel and no matter what you do.

The world is a better place because of

you, you,

you!

I hope you enjoyed reading about Kappy! Can I ask you a personal favor? Would you please write a review? It helps other readers decide if the book is something they would like to read.

If you want more information or would like to be the first to know about new books and special offers, visit my website at https://www.andicann.com .

Happy reading!

Andi

There are many other books by Andi Cann. Here are a few!

  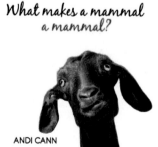

Published by MindView Press: Hibou

ISBN-13:   978-1-949761-23-8   eBook
ISBN-13:   978-1-949761-24-5   Paperback

Thank you for reading and for leaving a review!

Made in the USA
Las Vegas, NV
23 February 2024

Kappy loves being happy! Sometimes she's sad, though, and doesn't know what to do about it.

This sweet rhyming story with colorful pictures helps children understand that it's okay to feel sad and that there are ways to feel better!

ISBN 9781949761245

9781949 761245

9 0 0 0 0